Mud in Your Eye!

Mud in Your Eye!

Richard Ingrams & John Wells
Illustrated by Brian Bagnall

PRIVATE EYE/ANDRE DEUTSCH

Published in Great Britain by Private Eye Productions Ltd,
6 Carlisle Street, London W1

© 1987 Pressdram Ltd
Illustrations by Brian Bagnall © 1987

ISBN 233 98146 2

Printed by The Bath Press, Bath, Avon

10 Downing Street
Whitehall

27 JUNE 1986

Dear Bill,

Sorry I missed your Rotarian Wine and Cheese at the Stoat and Compasses, but we had to entertain a man called Deedes who has just got the boot (long overdue) from the Hot Seat at the *Telegraph* and been given a peerage to soothe the pain. A very motley gang assembled, including that very funny wizened old party from Robertsbridge who's always on the box groaning away about the hereafter in a weird suburban drawl. He didn't seem to have any very clear idea who I was, told me that in his opinion this Thatcher Woman was 'pretty barmy', and asked me whether I didn't long for death. Another case where abstention from hard liquor has clearly wreaked pretty good havoc with the little grey cells.

I am glad to say the Boss is standing firm on the Botha front. I got a very long aerogramme from Mrs Van der K. in Joburg thanking us for our continuing support over the sanctions and saying that Margaret's name is blessed as the one beacon of hope whenever a glass of Cape Sherry is raised in the Whites' Only Bar at the Smuts Arms. She says the news we're getting is all cooked up by the Pinkoes and that following PWB's very shrewd decision to bring out the big stick all the Red Clergy (except for that ghastly little comedian Tutu) have been put in the can and their troubles have instantly come to an end. The reptiles have apparently been told to confine their remarks to tomorrow's weather and the Tribal Come Dancing on the telly, a thoroughly sensible move in my view that would make things a great deal easier for M. were she to introduce similar measures here. As I said to her when the sanctions question cropped up over pre-prandial snorts at Chequers on Sunday, the only people who would get hurt would be innocent bystanders like the Major, who I happen to know is putting together a consignment of plastic bullets and grenades for that little nerve gas company he's a consultant with outside Birmingham. Think of the effect on unemployment if that order was put in jeopardy by a lot of religious maniacs meddling in things they have no idea about!

*'. . . including that very funny wizened old party
from Robertsbridge . . .'*

You probably saw that Runcieballs sent that tall bugger with
the blazer and the beard out there last week. Mark my words,
wherever that sod appears, trouble flares up overnight.

Talking of Mark, I slightly got the wind up when I read in
one of the rags that he has been thrown out of his luxury bedsit
in downtown Dallas. According to the Son and Heir, ever since
the Hopalong Lightning Raid on Colonel G., the neighbours
have got the wind up. They fear, so says the lad, that he and
therefore they will become the target for retaliatory strikes by
Muslim Fanatics, known to be no more accurate than the USAF.
That is his story anyway. In my opinion the little wimp is trying

to glamourise himself yet again, and the cause of his unpopularity probably lies in his antisocial habits, e.g. rudeness to his elders, revving up his fancy cars in the small hours and playing his James Last records too loud on his hi-fi equipment. So who can blame them for wanting to terminate his lease? My fear is that he will return to these shores and move in at Dulwich, but I suppose at my age one must be prone to these nightmare anxieties.

Bad news about the Argies booting us out of the World Cup. I watched it at the RAC with Maurice and his Air Malta stewardess, and we all got pretty emotional. Speaking as an expert, the referee had clearly been slipped a great deal of money to look the other way while Primadonna carried it into the net, and Maurice told me he'd read something in the paper about a previous occasion when the Argies had bribed the Peruvian Government several millions to throw the game away 6–0. Why, Maurice wanted to know, hadn't the Boss done the same? As usual, he went on and on about this, admittedly under provocation from some lawnmower reps in the bar, and finished up suggesting we should have offered them the Falklands in exchange for a straight win. In the end we had to call a minicab and the lady from Air Malta lost her hat on the way to the door.

See you in the bar behind the Centre Court.

Your old chum,

DENIS

 10 Downing Street
Whitehall

11 JULY 1986

Dear Bill,
Sorry to miss you at Wimbledon, but I got button-holed by a friend of Maurice's called Rickatson-Smythe who wanted me to host the opening ceremony at a Happy Diner Eatery on the M25, a task the Princess Michael of Kent had agreed to perform for a small fee but had dropped out of at the prospect of a ride up the river with Mr Branson. Talking of whom, you may have seen the Boss checked in on the same publicity stunt, though

9

what she sees in that ghastly bearded little creep with his tatty record shops and cheapo travel agency lowering the tone at Heathrow I have no idea. If it was left to me, the first thing any Clean-Up Britain Campaign would get its sharp stick into would be Master Branson, but I suppose to a woman who thinks the sun shines out of Jeffrey Archer's rearward parts, Branson must seem quite a little bobby-dazzler.

Do I sound bitter? Between you and me, the heat's been rather getting me down of late, and I may have been overdoing it on the quenching end of things. I was fast asleep the other afternoon when I was awoken with a nasty shock to find little Howe standing in front of me, apparently having shimmered in in his brothel-creepers undetected by Boris or any of the sleuths on duty. He peered owlishly round him for a few moments, fiddling with his tie, then suddenly became aware of my presence in the room. He explained he was actually looking for Margaret, to be briefed on his forthcoming trip to the troubled land of South Africa. As I waved him to a chair and mixed the Cabbage-flavoured Perrier with ice and lemon as requested, I couldn't help thinking what a lot of prats the Euros are. I mean the Veldt in flames, Kaffirs and Zulus running amok, Mrs Van der K. understandably distraught about finding reliable domestic staff, and who but a lot of woolly-minded foreigners would imagine that the arrival of Mogadon Man could somehow restore hope and re-establish normality?

I was about to comment on how beautiful the garden was looking, when the Boss herself swept in, gave me a withering look and an even more withering one to our double-chinned plenipotentiary. 'So you're going, Geoffrey,' she began. 'Please don't interrupt me. So long as you realise that you and your European friends will achieve precisely nothing. I have made it clear that my opposition to Sanctions remains unwavering. The Party is firmly behind me on this as you will have been aware from last night's debate in the House.' Apparently Old Silly Billy with the Eyebrows had come back from South Africa with his tasteful matt enlargements of urban squalor and was attempting to put the boot in, accusing the Boss of playing Chamberlain to Botha's Hitler, when Margaret, primed by one of her back-room beavers KO'd the Koala with a line of his own in Cabinet some years back, arguing in favour of flogging arms to Pretoria.

Otherwise our lot have been busy back-tracking on the Water-

'Branson must seem quite a little bobby-dazzler . . .'

front. Matey next door had some damnfool plan to raise a bit of wind for his next round of tax cuts by flogging off the sewers and waterworks to Trust House Forte. (You may remember he had the same idea about British Airways.) Anyhow, Fatso appears to have discovered late in the day that someone else already owned them, i.e. the local councils, and that in any case it was only going to lose them a lot of votes. So poor little Ridley had to get up and explain that it was all being put on the back burner as there were more important issues in the pipeline, though what they were he couldn't quite remember at the moment. Ditto the BBC. M. was determined finally to clobber that band of self-satisfied pinkoes by making them take adverts like everybody else. So she hired some tame egghead to compile the necessary evidence, and blow me, egghead and his little panel of unemployment loons singularly failed to deliver the goods.

Did Maurice send you that very brightly-coloured prospectus about his time-sharing scheme in the Algarve? I got out my calculator and peered at the small print and, as far as I can see, one is looking at two weekends at the so-far unconstructed Casa-Condominio-Pic with breathtaking views of the sea (through the telescope on the Links) for a mere twenty-five grand, not counting the hidden extras. I fear a lot of chaps are going to get their fingers burned on this one, including Prosser-Cluff's brother-in-law, who's obviously fallen for the sales spiel from Maurice's Air Malta lady, and already parted with his life-savings.

More anon,
Yours,

DENIS

10 Downing Street
Whitehall

25 JULY 1986

Dear Bill,
I had another letter from Mrs Van der Kefferbescher at the weekend which I have to say brought tears to my eyes. 'I would just like you to know,' she says, 'that all of us here in Pretoria hold your wife in the highest esteem. After Service on Sunday

our Pastor, Rev. Sjambok, asked the congregation to give thanks to God for what Margaret Thatcher has done to preserve us all from the forces of darkness now threatening to overthrow the Dutch Reformed Church and our whole way of life. I tell you, Denis, the atmosphere was electrical. All the Army Veterans were wearing full medals and many a frail old hand rose spontaneously to the salute at the mention of her name.'

When you read that sort of thing it makes you feel that somehow it's all been worthwhile.

The BBC, of course, as I may have said before, are all fully paid up members of the Communist Party and every night on the news they've been making a big ballyhoo about the Commonwealth Games, suggesting the whole event is going to have to be scrubbed just because a few dusky pole-vaulters lost their bottle at the last minute. I happen to know that the Games lark is a publicity stunt run up by that awful fat man with the five double chins who runs the *Daily Mirror*, and who just between ourselves is, according to Boris, one of 'them'. Quite honestly, Bill, who gives a toss anyway about a lot of foreign Johnnies pounding round the asphalt up in Edinburgh, especially when the Open's on at Turnberry?

This Commonwealth caper has always struck me as very much a dead duck. Of course it was another thing in the days of the Empire when John Bull wielded the big stick over Lesser Breeds without the Law and everything was tickety-boo. Now it's a free-for-all with a lot of barmy dictators waving fly-whisks and lecturing us on the values of democracy, it makes you vomit, quite honestly. I met a lot of those Johnnies in the old days when they were either in and out of chokey or serving drinks in the Mess, and quite frankly I wouldn't trust any of them with my clubs. Margaret and I have always seen very much eye to eye on this, and I like to think I have been quite a support to the old girl over the years.

The nigger in the woodpile, if one can use such a term without being immediately clapped into jail, is the Queen. Extraordinarily enough for a relatively intelligent woman in middle life who's knocked about a bit, she's always had a soft spot for Kaunda and Nyerere and all the rest of the Moscow State Circus. Since this sanctions business blew up they've all been on the blower to the Royal Apartments urging the Great White Mother to give Margaret a boot up the arse. As you probably know she's not officially allowed to interfere in the running of the show, but

'. . . I spent a pretty grisly morning in Moss Bros . . .'

she bloody well does. The Boss has to go round there every week
and tell her what's cooking. It's meant to be a formality and
she's supposed to pass everything on the nod just like the old
Chairman at Burma. In fact she's abysmally rude to Margaret,
often keeps her standing around while she finishes writing her
thankyou letters, then asks her a lot of pretty beady questions.
Some of these are quite sound – Why don't they string up Scargill
etc? – but on the sanctions business it's been one long *Guardian*
sermon after another about the need to love our fellow men.

The Boss got back very white and shakey from last week's

session, having gone the full fifteen rounds, losing her gumshield but claiming that she'd won on points. M. may have been a little unwise, after having to listen to half an hour of Lefty tosh from the Throne, in suggesting that she might have to reconsider the Civil List. One consequence was that when we got our tickets for the Andie and Fergie Wedding Show, we discovered that we were in Side Row L, which Boris says is between the Malawi High Commissioner and the King of Tonga, who, he says, needs three seats and has only been allotted the one. I spent a pretty grisly morning in Moss Bros being fitted up with the kit in the company of a lot of malodorous American tourists hiring sporrans, and will give you a full account of the vulgar shenanigans in my next.

Did you hear that Maurice flew out a lot of soaks to the Algarve to write up his Time-sharing Wheeze in the Sundays? Apparently they all got legless and the only publicity he got back for the five grand he put into it was one para in Eddie Shah's *Sunday Today* hinting that it was the new haven for wanted criminals from the Costa del Crook.

Sayonara old chum,

DENIS

 10 Downing Street
Whitehall
8 AUGUST 1986

Dear Bill,
M. was very grateful for your jumbo-sized Get Well card re her contracting finger, but the fact of the matter is that it was a bit premature. She's not due to be wheeled into the theatre until after the Black and White Minstrel Show a.k.a. the Commonwealth Conference. I ran into Dr O'Gooley at the Army and Navy Club the other lunchtime and he filled me in on the condition over a couple of G and Ts. Odd thing is, according to the Doc, that it's something that very often crops up in alcoholics and is known in the trade as Wino's Finger. I said I thought in the Boss's case it had been brought on by too many Masonic hand-

shakes and we had a good laugh over that until asked to keep it down a bit by the Brigadier, the Club Secretary.

Boss is still holding out on the Sanctions. Surprisingly, old Van der Pump, the South African Rasputin who reads her tea-leaves, turns out to be very sound on the question. He rang up the other night, having had a news flash from the subconscious in the form of a dream after lunch. In the dream he had seen a Springbok, which he took to represent the land of his birth, being stalked by a large and ferocious bear. Suddenly a beautiful blonde woman swings down on a creeper, wrestles with the bear for some moments to Van der P's cries of encouragement, and eventually biffs it on the nose, causing it to skulk back into the jungle. This he interpreted as a clear indication that Margaret must stick firmly to her guns in order to defeat the menace of world communism. M. thanked him profusely, and said couldn't he have a word with the Palace as he's very thick with the Son and Heir and reads his tea-leaves as well.

Talking of which, the bit of strife I mentioned in my last between M. and H.M. for some reason got picked up by the reptiles on the *Sunday Times* who blew it all up into an enormous how's-your-father in order to try and stem the avalanche of fall-ing circulation figures. Luckily for me – did you show my letter to anyone? – the blame was eventually shouldered by some Scotch Johnny at the Buck House Press Office, who should have known better than pass the time of day with the little bugger responsible, who turned out to be the very same piece of filth who wangled my bank statements out of one of Furniss's minions at the NatWest, blast his eyes.

None of which has helped relations between our two royal houses. We had to go North last week to show the flag in Edinburgh at the Comic Olympics, which involved accepting a hot dinner off the Windsors at Holyrood House. The usual humiliations and tedium, the Queen having laid on the bagpipes from the moment we took up the EPNS, which drowned all small-talk and left me hoarse from shouting about Fergie and her ghastly sailor to some miserable old Duchess from Fifeshire.

The next day M. was due to present gongs to the handful of competitors still remaining, bringing us into unpleasantly close proximity with that frightful tub of lard Maxwell who owns the *Daily Mirror* and who has been bragging over the last few weeks that he'd persuaded some trouser manufacturer friend of Maurice's to cough up the shortfall. Unfortunately, as he beam-

'. . . M. was very grateful for your jumbo-sized Get Well card . . .'

ingly announced to M. over a goblet of bad champagne in the VIP viewing lounge, this (surprise, surprise) had fallen through and he was accordingly sending the chitty round to Number Eleven for prompt settlement. Gamma Rays were turned on, but the ebullient Czech is clearly immune.

I assume you had a full account from Maurice of the wedding. He cleaned up with his Fergieburger stands which may have offset the Timeshare disaster. Personally I found the whole thing pretty ballsaching. As predicted they made jolly sure we were stuck behind a pillar and had to hobnob with Kinnock and his CND wife for the best part of two hours while they pissed about fiddling with the wedding dress. That Ferguson man is obviously loaded, and I told Carol afterwards that she couldn't expect anything of that nature in the unlikely event of her pulling herself together and finding the appropriate wimp. As for Mark, words fail me. M. got a bill from his Public Relations firm in the U.S. the other day that would have covered my green fees for fifteen years. I can't tell you where we're going on holiday for security reasons, but it won't be the Azores.

Vivat Regina,
   Yours,

DENIS

DUNBOOZIN
  SEAVIEW TERRACE
    TREFELLONA
      CORNWALL   22 AUGUST 1986

Dear Bill,

As you can see, our little caravan has come to rest in this quiet Cornish Cove, where there is no sound at dusk but the crackle of the policemen's walkie-talkies and the beach is deserted if one ignores the presence of four or five hundred reptiles from the world's press leaving the place littered with empty bottles of methylated spirit and shooting off flashbulbs every time one goes for a pee in the middle of the night. A pretty grisly hole to find oneself in, especially with the wind and rain driving in from the Atlantic, and the nearest hostelry ten miles away full of awful trippers playing space invaders and sucking cornets in the Saloon Bar. The only solace is that one isn't at Schloss Bangelstein closeted with the Widow Glover and dreading the onset of an evening with the weirdoes at the Festspielhaus, Herr von Karavan (Iron Cross and Oakleaves) bowing and scraping all the way to the exit.

M's little op seems to have gone off quite smoothly, Downing Street knee-deep in Get Well cards, fruit and flowers from the Saatchis, together with a sprig of withered chrysanths from the Palace and a printed card from H.M. the Queen wishing the

Boss a speedy release from her present troubles. I don't know whether you saw the lady in question jogging up five hundred steps at Auchtermuchty Lighthouse to prove that there was nothing wrong with her ticker – clearly timed to make the Boss look a crock? Not to be outdone, Margaret threw away her sling for the photocall and ran about the beach like a wild thing, waving her arms and playing with some damnfool dog the Saatchis had hired for the day from Rentapet. Needless to say the Press were not allowed to record the touching scene later in the day of yours truly chopping up her grub and turning over the pages of her new Jeffrey Archer.

Prior to all that, there was another upandadowner with Munster. That very sozzled old coot Whitelaw who's got the wind up about a Labour Landslide staggered round a couple of weeks back having fortified himself en route at various saloons, to stir things up again about poor Norman. Very rough diamond, not one of us, alienating our people in the shires, possible appeal to used car salesmen but otherwise a minus factor. Some word of this must have got back to Munster, as he was soon on the blower, once again proffering his resignation and saying that if his services weren't required he had a perfectly good job to go to flying Mustangs for the Libyans. Boss clearly had half a mind to call the bugger's bluff, but with the present shortage of chaps to man the parapet she clearly came to the conclusion that it was better to have him inside pissing out than outside pissing in.

Anyhow I heard her ringing him back to say that he had her fullest confidence, greatly appreciated all that he had done and was doing for the Party and that a good rest somewhere out of the limelight would do him the world of good. From her sudden change of tone I suspect he may have suggested the same was true in her own case, for I heard her growl a brief word to the effect that holidays were not for her and that a Prime Minister's work was never done.

Another bone of contention on the Munster front is the Corsican Question. According to M., Alberto and Luigi Saatchi are all washed up and have lost focus on the Product. So Central Office have got a tender in from a new lot of greasers with an American Consumer Profiling Service developed by Billy Graham. This does away with all the old-fashioned ABC for Knobs and Yobs, car-owning and second home buyers, and stresses instead the positive Blow-You-Jack attitudes of what are known as Belongers. You and I for example are Belongers, Maurice is not. Daphne

'. . . playing with some damnfool dog the Saatchis had hired . . .'

is, Maurice's Air Malta lady is not. His old antique hyperlady is on the borderline. All a lot of balls if you ask me.

I'm going to be down at Dulwich for a bit while the Boss traipses round C & A ordering the fittings and fabrics. If you'd care to slope over any morning that suits you, the bar facilities are already in situ and we might get a few holes after lunch. I'm glad to say that no expense has been spared on the insulated alcohol store.

Are you going to Maurice's Car Boot Sale on Sunday? I toyed with the idea but quite honestly the M25 is hell on wheels in August and I'm beginning to think that Maurice may drink a little too much. Has the same thought ever crossed your mind?

Have fun in Tenerife. My sister Joyce used to go there for the eurhythmics before the War.

May Allah step lightly on your head,

DENIS

10 Downing Street
Whitehall

19 SEPTEMBER 1986

Dear Bill,

Did you get my p.c. of the Flashing Troll from Oslo? It did cross my mind to put it in an envelope, but I thought it would be more amusing to let the postman hand it over to Daphne. As you may have seen, we had a pretty rough ride in Norway with a lot of Lefty hooligans stoned out of their minds on glue, alcohol being in short supply due to the suicide rate. I thought it a bit rich, this Nordic rabble trying to tell M. what's what about Apartheid when they've never seen a black face in their lives. Talking of which, did you see that super-prat Runcie on the TV tangoing round the floor with little Tutu? Mrs Van der K. was terribly upset, and wrote to me saying did Runcie know that the crypt of Desmond T's Cathedral was choc-a-bloc with Russian-made machine guns? I passed the message on to Hurd, but he was pretty snooty, saying I sounded as though I'd had a good lunch and why didn't I ring in the morning?

Her Scandatour all came as a bit of a blow to the Boss, as Saatchis had told her she could use Norway to make the Autumn Campaign Launch, majoring on her new 'Green' image for which she has already coughed up six hundred million, fitting strainers to power stations. However the Norwegians weren't in the least bit grateful and we didn't at all take to Mrs Brundtland, a sort of Norwegian version of Glenys Kinnock who spent the whole time haranguing us in broken Svensk about her ideas for curing unemployment in the UK, and the advantages of log stoves over nuclear fuel.

You may wonder why the Cabinet has remained unscathed after all the big talk of a major reshuffle. Personally I told M. to get rid of Matey next door, Howe, Whitelaw – a drunken old deadbeat if ever there was (though it takes one to know one you might say) – also Hogg and Hurd, on the obvious grounds that no decent company would have them on the board. But the Corsican Twins unrolled a big screed about the Nostalgia Factor, and how in times of turbulence the consumer will turn to the tried and tested product, i.e. Marmite, Ovaltine, Whitelaw. So all we got in the end was a lot of shuffling about in the lower

6.

'. . . *Runcie tangoing round the floor with little Tutu . . .*'

reaches and a very tiresome loudmouthed woman in black stockings brought in to do PR for the NHS. Take one look at her and join BUPA, was my view, though when I heard what happened to Maurice's friend in the private clinic when they took out the wrong bit and he passed over, it did make one ponder.

You see they've finally got round to flogging off BA, carefully timed to coincide with the inquest on last year's air disaster. The Boss is frightfully keen on the man in charge, this Lord King johnny, an amiable enough old buffer who's thrown several thousand stewards out of work and speeded up the luggage carousels at Gatwick. According to Furniss at the NatWest it's going dirt cheap, but even so he doesn't recommend it as a flutter. Boss however is now dead set on shunting King on to the BBC to strip off a few of their assets. If it can put the cat among the pigeons in that nest of overweight Trotskyite gayboys and wipe the smile off that Irish one who's always on in the evenings for a start, then he'll certainly have my support, and I might persuade a few of Mrs Van der Kafferbesher's friends to buy a majority shareholding in BBC plc when it's finally slimmed down and up for grabs.

Must stop now, as Van der Pump is coming round for a chin-wag on the South African situation. Boris is making a leek quiche, which is Van der P's favourite grub, I've opened a bottle of Chateau Lamberhurst, and after supper we're all going to hold hands in a darkened room and try to contact General Smuts for advice.

Yours on the ethereal plane,

DENIS

10 Downing Street
Whitehall

3 OCTOBER 1986

Dear Bill,

As you can imagine, everyone here at HQ is pretty cock-a-hoop at the Two Davids falling out over the Bomb. Even Margaret allowed herself a few moments to relax of an afternoon, making me switch off the golf and tune in to Eastbourne for a chuckle. I must say, one look at those lemonade-swilling CND shirt-lifters and you could tell they'd come apart in the first breeze. Little Steel, who thought he'd got the whole thing sewn up, sitting on the platform obviously rubbing his hands in anticipation of a kiss and cuddle climax with the SDP, took no end of a knock. Serve the little bugger right is what I say. Why can't he leave it all to Margaret and sod off back to running a tam o'shanter stall in Auchtermuchty which is all he's good for?

You could see the Doctor johnny was pretty miffed too, especially after having to control his very natural student-throttling instincts when he addressed the weirdoes earlier in the week. In point of fact Owen has always been very sound on the Bear, and should by rights be on our side and not wasting his time with the various fat old winos you see littered about their platform with nowhere to go. It all goes to show that the Boss has been right all along in taking an electrified cattle-prod to Gorblimov. Whatever Boris may say, he's finally got the message and is now clearly prepared to talk turkey with Hopalong.

Talking of which, I happened to hear on the wireless when I was in the bath this morning that the Stock Exchange has opened again in Shanghai. Didn't Prosser-Cluff's father do very well for himself out there between the wars? I thought it might be an opening for Maurice P., but he was very shirty when I rang him and still seems to be having a bit of strife offloading his Time-share customers from Portugal. One of them, a retired Brigadier in the Gurkhas, has actually pitched a tent on his lawn and is refusing to budge until he is reimbursed in cash. Apparently he shakes his fist at Maurice's Air Malta lady and growls at her whenever she goes out shopping.

Did you see the Royals on TV? After all the trouble we had with the Two Hundred and Fifty Years of Number Ten Show

24

'. . . a retired Brigadier in the Gurkhas, has actually pitched a
tent on his lawn . . .'

I could have warned them not to let those greasy little buggers in the leather jackets through the barbed wire. Even with the help of Sir Alastair Browntongue, that prize creamer who used to do the news alongside the other piss-artist in the toupee who turned his toes up some years back (a terrible warning to us all), it was pretty grisly stuff. She was made to look like some sort of Page Three Cutie with clothes on, whereas I've found her rather a sweet little poppet when we've been sitting next to one another at Balmoral. Always laughs at my stories, even when I forget the punchline. He, of course, came over as a prize wally traipsing about with a lot of ghastly do-gooders and coons when he should have been presenting gongs for gallantry to prison warders. I may have nodded off at one point when they were standing at an airport at seven o'clock in the morning talking to some tall brown fellow who appeared to have put his trousers on the wrong way up. When I came to he was pottering round the kitchen garden talking about dandelion soup to some long-haired hippy in blue check trousers and a cook's hat. If you ask me Van der Pump has got a lot to answer for, filling his head with nonsense about the strange world of the little Bushmen and all that class of caper.

Did you get your TSB shares all right? I told Lawson to let you go through to the front of the queue, but he never pays a blind bit of attention to what I say and the last I heard they were picking them out of a hat like one of Daphne's raffles. Maurice, who got spotted on the video trying to come back a fourth time in a different hat, had all his application forms torn up and will appear in court later in the month.

You saw the Argies thrashed us at St Andrews? Pretty black day when that shower can knock clean-living British golfers into a cocked hat. I said to Margaret they should have a drug test. Bet you anything you like they'd been sniffing Tippex in the changing room before they drove off.

Conference looms. Let me know your movements. I was thinking of getting a chitty from O'Gooley to be excused boots, in which case I could join you on the Algarve for a few days R & R chez the Widow Flack.

DENIS

'... frantic trips to the Acousti-booth in the Main Foyer ...'

Dear Bill,

You were quite right when you said we'd have been better off in the Algarve than bloody Bournemouth. I should have known your hip flask would set off a full-scale terror warning at the revolving doors, and considering they blew a million quid making sure M. came to no harm, it's hardly surprising you got duffed over by fifteen of those mad buggers with the baseball bats. I literally had to step over two burly constables sleeping across the threshold of the bathroom every time I went to the toilet in the night, and when one has had a few it's quite difficult to keep one's balance.

Not that there was much going in the way of sleep, most of the small hours being occupied with creating Margaret's Blockbuster Tirade to enthuse the troops on the final day. 'Midnight oil is the name of the game,' said one of the Corsicans' minions as he took another sheaf of gags from poor old

Sir Custard-face who was toiling away in a shantung dressing gown over his word processor with only a Trusthouse Forteburger and a box of Cotes de Maroc to sustain him. 'Every year it gets more and more difficult,' he vouchsafed to me, puffing on his eight-inch amber cigarette-holder. 'As one grows older, the Muse is more and more recalcitrant, don't you find? Luckily one has in the First Lady a true pro with a wonderful sense of timing.' Realising I was going to have to put up with a full night of this sort of rubbish, I turned on a video of Wentworth and asked Boris to take my hip flask down to the Francis Drake Bar and fill her up with Four Star.

I couldn't resist a chuckle watching Lawson sweating over the Full English Breakfast at £13.95 as he scanned the *FT* for the latest news from the City. The problem throughout the troubled week, as you probably gathered from your broker Pinter, was that the pound was being hammered by the Nips and practically everybody else, forcing Mr Nicely to jack up interest rates in order to stem the flow. As you can imagine, this would have struck a rather unfortunate note just when they were trumpeting their great Economy on the Move Again, Getting Inflation Down and Creating More Jobs. Hence Lawson's frantic trips to the Acousti-booth in the Main Foyer, ringing up Leigh-Pemberton at the Bank of England and asking him to hold the rates down until the last delegates had been shovelled on to the train home with M's speech still ringing in their ears.

All in all I found it harder to stay awake than ever. Willie Whitelaw had to slip the TV cameramen a tenner apiece not to catch him fast asleep with his mouth wide open, though I fear they may have shown yours truly having a bit of a snigger when Hurd was being booed. Serve the little bugger right. I've told him again and again that the only way to get the crime rate down is to bring back the rope and the birch and scrap all this nonsense about Community Service. I don't know whether the Major has told you what happened to his mother when some Borstal Boys were sent round to paint her greenhouse. When she looked out of the window the greenhouse had gone – along with the lags.

Talking of Labour, I don't know if you saw Kinnock's little shindig at Blackpool. One of the reptiles who'd been up there showed me the coloured brochure they were handing out, produced by their equivalent of the Corsican Twins: tea towels and willie warmers the faithful could buy to give their gay friends for Christmas, bringing in dibs to party funds: pin-ups of Glenys wearing her CND badge, Where To Eat in Blackpool by Egon Ronay etc, etc, all tastefully wrapped in a shiny folderette with that damnfool rose on the front. Paid for by Moscow it goes without saying. Boris told me that Blackpool was crawling with Gorblimov's men, buying everyone drinks and making sure they'd send the Yanks packing the moment they moved in. I couldn't make it out quite honestly: Scargill and Benn sitting there wreathed in smiles. It looked to me like one of Maurice's sales conventions for hygienic tissues. 'Make sure your toilet's odour-free, With Red Rose Flavour Labour Partee.' The whole thing makes you want to vomit.

Margaret was very miffed with Hopalong grabbing the headlines right in the middle of the conference with all this summitry in Iceland. Gorblimov didn't make it any better with his nautical capers, any seaworthy Soviet vessel these days being bound to collide with something or blow up in mid-ocean. Hopalong is still in fairly bad odour with the Boss for having let the Senate railroad him over South Africa, leaving her as sole defender of PWB in his heroic stand against the forces of darkness.

I ran into that silly Currie woman in the hotel lobby and gave her a piece of my mind. There's far too much balderdash talked nowadays to my mind about what people ought to eat and drink. She should come round to the RAC at lunchtime one day and watch the boys tucking into the Club steak and kidney with treacle pud swilled down with half a bottle of eyewash and a magnum of plonk and see where she can put her nut cutlets. I shouldn't think she'll last long. The Boss has cornered the Miss Piggy end of the market and she's never really been one for understudies.

Hasta luego mi amigo,

DENIS

P.S. Try saying the name of the Icelandic premier when you've had a few.

10 Downing Street
Whitehall

31 OCTOBER 1986

Dear Bill,

Don't say I didn't warn you or indeed the Boss on numerous occasions. The moment I clapped eyes on that little greaser Archer I knew he was a wrong 'un. Anyone who's got their knees brown in commerce can spot that type of chancer a mile away. Smile going on and off like a neon sign, shiny suit, hair always freshly shampooed, a wallet full of share certificates he tries to palm you off with, and a lot of bullshit about all of his wonderful achievements in the field of literature and high finance.

The Boss however never learnt her lesson after Smarmy Cecil. She bought one of Archer's books at Gatwick to read on the plane and was bowled over by the glamour of it all. Next thing we knew he was on the strength, number two to Mr Munster over whose sensitive corns he proceeded to trample like a drug-crazed chimpanzee. Neither of them the best of casting – as I remember remarking at the time – when it came to convincing the public of our essential moral wholesomeness, old world charm etc. No sooner en poste than the little swine was up on his hind legs in front of the media repeating a lot of things he'd heard me say in the bar, i.e. Unemployment all got up by the newspapers, most of the three million workshy scroungers being subsidised by good honest nine to fivers like yourself and Maurice Picarda etc. After that they did their best to plug him with a dummy and he was officially sent out into the field to 'Stimulate the grass roots', i.e. plug his books to the Funny Hat Brigade after lunch.

Boris tipped me off months ago on a Vodka tasting at the Russian Embassy that his lot had been tapping Archer's phone for some time, the word being that his menage was not as regular as it might be, working wife living in Cambridge and so forth. I'd also picked up a whisper at Bournemouth that the reptiles were on his trail, following a tip-off from some seedy little wog in Wimbledon who claimed to have spotted him hanging about in Shepherd's Market perusing the cards in the newsagents' windows.

As far as I can piece it together from the *Daily Telegraph* –

'. . . spotted him hanging about in Shepherd's Market . . .'

and what a mess that is nowadays – this tuppenny-ha'penny tarterino, probably with a screw loose, was making trouble up and down Fleet Street, saying she'd dispensed a shilling's worth to someone closely resembling the accused, and wouldn't be averse to a fifteen figure fee for her disclosures. Instead of telling her and the malodorous organ involved to go and jump in the Thames, Archer began to behave like one of the characters in his own rubbishy paperbacks – if his own indeed they be – and when some ass in a striped shirt told him he could scotch the whole business for a couple of grand handed over in used ones under the clock at Victoria on the stroke of midnight, he couldn't resist the scenario. Stupid prat.

None of this came exactly as treacle to the ears of the Boss who snatched up the blower at nine o'clock prompt to shatter the peace of Mr Munster's Sunday lie-in at his little hideaway in Potter's Bar. Force Eight on the Richter Scale, why hadn't she been warned, she'd always had her suspicions about Archer, this was all Munster's fault, if only Cecil had been there none of this would have happened. It was obvious from the momentary pause in the lava flow that Munster had been unable to resist pointing out that Smarmy C. had also been caught with his pants down. 'How dare you compare that Knight Errant with this seedy soft porn pedlar! Don't lecture me, Norman, about the old values. You foisted Archer on us against all my instincts. His record should have told you that he was unreliable. No, I do not want Gummer back!' At this she terminated the conversation, and before I could get out turned all eight barrels on me for what she called my dewy-eyed innocence in backing men like Archer, no doubt because I was a devotee of his books.

Poor old Munster. I couldn't help feeling a moment's solidarity with our blue-jowled pilot friend. There he was, grabbing a quiet weekend amid the rigours of proving once and for all that Kate Adie is in the pay of Gadaffi and laying plans for flogging off the BBC in the wake of the Gas and British Airways, when this pile of ordure is fed into his air-conditioning.

Archer himself, the little hero of the hour, inevitably sent round a barrowload of red roses and a nauseating note saying that the whole story was totally untrue but wishing to spare Margaret even a moment of embarrassment, he was sacrificing his career and all he had on the altar of his first and only true love. This was torn into shreds, and I was given the flowers to put on the compost heap. Sic transit Gloria Hunniford.

See you at Maurice's bonfire party at the Redundant Church.

Yours aye,

DENIS

10 Downing Street
Whitehall

14 NOVEMBER 1986

Dear Bill,

Hats off to Mr Munster! I may have had my reservations in the past about his not being absolutely out of the top drawer, but the way he's gone after the pinko shirtlifters at the BBC is absolutely first-rate. I remember that night Hoppo zapped Gadaffi with the Boss's help and encouragement, and I well recall that Adie woman weeping and wailing just because a few hooligan wogs had bought it when some hospital had blown up. According to Barnstormer at the American Embassy this was entirely due to one of Gadaffi's own hand-held missiles going rogue thanks to typical Middle Eastern incompetence. This fact was not brought out at all in the broadcast, and it was made to look as if the Boss was the only political leader who supported Hopalong, when actually there were quite a lot of others, whose names I can't at the moment recall, who were rooting for the old gun-slinger.

Now the Trots in charge at Broadcasting House are trying to wriggle out of it, blinding poor Munster with statistics, but the public won't be taken in. I was down at the Club Friday lunchtime and one of Maurice's friends told me they all thought Munster had won game set and match and that the least the BBC could do was to string the Adie woman up by the thumbs and bring someone like Prosser-Cluff in to clear the Pinkoes out root and branch. This chappie with the gammy leg they've put in charge now who used to run around for Rupert Murdoch will be damn all use. P.C. would have a much more sensible attitude. When he was in Kuala Lumpur, some local Commie slit-eyes infiltrated the staff magazine and started filling it with Marxist propaganda and a lot of damn fool cartoons showing P.C. swinging from a tree with a whisky bottle jammed between his teeth. Within five minutes of the issue in question landing on his desk, Prosser-Cluff pulped every copy, burned down the offices and bulldozed the printing plant, which as I've often said is the only language these bastards understand. The name of the game is grasping the nettle.

I popped in on Furniss this morning to take a shufty at various

'. . . and bulldozed the printing plant . . .'

bottom lines, and hear his views on Mr Nicely Nicely's U-turn. They've shunted the poor old boy out of his panelled office to make way for a new computer and put him in some makeshift Portakabin in what used to be the Foreign Department on the first floor, so he wasn't in the best of moods, despite the presence of a cardboard crate of Marks and Sparks Amontillado that seemed to have taken a pretty good hammering before I arrived. He said the punters had heard it all before from our fat friend at Number Eleven: pre-election handouts for all, big tax cuts on the way, molto optimistico, boom, boom, boom. In fact, according to Furniss, all the money boys have rumbled old Fatso long ago and are now openly expressing the view that he should get back to tipping shares at the *Sunday Telegraph*. Not that he was any good at that either, but at least he was no serious danger to shipping.

Whilst on the subject of LSD, I understand the Major came a cropper in the Big Bang. His broker, some awful yob in a suit from Farnham, was just shunting the old boy's funds out of Tokyo and into Shanghai when the black and white telly he was working on suddenly blew a fuse and when it came on again they couldn't find the Major's savings anywhere. I told Furniss about it, and we both had a good laugh.

Apparently Hoppo has come unstuck at last with all his lot getting the bum's rush in the mid-term elections. Fortunately he has no idea what's going on, so it won't darken his declining years, and anyway he hasn't been running the show for a long time. It's more like that Spanish cove in the history books who turned up his toes doing battle with the wog, but they strapped his mortal remains right way up on a gee-gee and had him out in front to keep morale up with the rank and file. Result Spain 4, Wogs 0.

Talking of hasbeens, what price Old Oystereyes being put in charge of the clap clinic? When this ghastly AIDS business first blew up, I asked O'Gooley whether there was any danger, and his view was that chaps of our age had got it coming to us anyway and that should the odd tartarino come to hand one might as well go out with a bang. Now however they've started to get the wind up, not just the FO at risk etc. So the most promiscuous elements, i.e. the Armed Services, Cabinet etc are to be circulated with the appropriate pamphlets. Maurice has bought a lot of shares in a rubber johnny company in Taiwan, and once they start advertising on the TV he reckons they'll go through the roof.

Very hard luck on Maurice, his Guy Fawkes Party going the way it did. Some of the fire appliances came from as far afield as Deal, and the chief firewallah told me Maurice should have known not to use dynamite for starting a bonfire. If you want to visit him he's in the Nabarro Ward in E Wing.

DENIS

P.S. Fingers crossed on the Mark-and-his-new-Texan-floozie-front!

Dear Bill,
Thank you for your congratulatory card on Mark's engagement to Miss Bunkoff. I think we may indeed have got rid of the little bugger this time round, but I'm not banking on it until the sky pilot has said the magic words and the Wedding March blows out of the Muzak Box. As you may have seen we played host to the happy couple and all the reptiles were marshalled round to take their snaps. To the little sod's utter amazement, M. refused to stump up for the ring, so he had to go out and buy a cheapie from the U.S. equivalent of Bravington's, hence his disinclination to allow them a quick flash of one of the smallest pieces of cut glass I have ever seen in my life.

None of this seemed to make the slightest impression on Miss Burger, who struck me as being even dopier than her intended. I think this may have been what Charlie Whackett had in mind when

'. . . hiding behind that Holy Joe sidekick of Runcie's . . .'

he set up the love match in the first place, anyone having to be pretty solid mutton between the ears not to spot the boy Mark coming a mile off. Charlie told me that the Burgeroffs are in the same line of business as he is, automobile marketing consultancy, i.e. shifting a lot of reconditioned motorway wreckage to any punter mug enough to buy it. Old Pa Burgerstand has made a pretty pile out of this since he got off the banana boat from Dusseldorf, and has flogged off more old crocks than you and I have downed large ones at the RAC, so there's no shortage of readies in their little old used car lot in the West, where with any luck the son and heir will put down roots too deep ever to be disturbed again.

Meanwhile poor little Carol has been having a ghastly time at the *Telegraph*. You may recall that nice old boy who took her on – Pritchett? Deedes? some name like that – tartan socks, short trousers, and a funny way of talking as if he's sloshed which he is most of the time – anyway, he was put out to grass by the new owners. In his place they recruited some ghastly war buff called Hastings whose old man used to do stunts in a children's comic. This Hastings has been throwing his weight around a good deal, making himself generally unpopular and changing the paper about so you don't know where to find the Morons' Crossword anymore.

Little Carol, in all innocence, had been off to interview that big German woman there's been all this trouble about for copying out chunks of other people's books, sold it to *Women's Thing* for quite a lot of money, and then had Hastings stamping and screaming in her face, asking why hadn't she done it for the *Daily Telegraph*. She quite rightly pointed out that nobody, not even Marie Christine von Ribbentropp, would have agreed to see her if she'd said she was from the *Telegraph*, at which point Hastings made various unforgivable remarks and the matter is now in the hands of the legal fraternity; hence M's shortage of any petty cash to pay for engagement rings.

So much for the Home Front. What of Hopalong, you enquire? If you ask me, the old boy's finally been rumbled on the Honest Hoppo the Brave Bold Sheriff in the White Hat routine. He told them all with his hand on his heart he would never trade in human flesh: now of course it turns out they've been flogging bazookas to the Ayatollah hiding behind that Holy Joe sidekick of Runcie's with the beard.

Talking of egg on face, have you been following the Affair

of Sir Robert Armstrong? They sent him out to Australia, very misguidedly in my view, to stop some ex-MI5 weirdo from spilling the beans in his memoirs, and the Ozzies have very understandably told him to go and stick his head up a dead bear's bum, such is the colourful parlance of the judiciary in those parts. Boris and I had a pretty good chuckle over it, as we know Armstrong of old, a shifty-looking greaser who used to hang about in the pantry here at Number Ten ogling Mrs Barstow, our erstwhile cook. I would have given him his marching orders then and there, dirty fellow.

Cares of state apart, the Boss has been running round like a headless chicken organising an eightieth birthday thrash for Van der Pump, Soothsayer in Ordinary to his Royal Highness Prince Bigears. The old boy is very excited about the celebrations and rang the other morning clearly pretty miffed to get me instead of the Boss, but nonetheless overflowing with travellers' lore. Did I know that in the Kalahari, when the Chief Witch Doctor reaches four score years, all the other Bushmen and Bushwomen for miles around cover their heads with cowdung and set up a curious wailing that often lasts for two or three weeks? I said he wouldn't get that kind of malarkey at Downing Street and he'd be bloody lucky to be given a glass of warm sherry courtesy the Ministry of the Environment.

I'll let you know how it goes on the night.

Yours till the drums stop beating,

DENIS

10 Downing Street
Whitehall

12 DECEMBER 1986

Dear Bill,

I wish I could answer the questions you raise in your p.c. re the MI5 case. I have just had a long session with Boris in the pantry and must confess that I am none the wiser. None the wiser, you may say, but considerably more inebriated. Touche, as the man said when his wife cut his head off with the breadknife.

Apparently it all started with this retired 007 Johnny, name

*'. . . now living in Oz and trying to raise a few bob on his
memoirs . . .'*

of Wright now living in Oz and trying to raise a few bob on
his memoirs. His central theme was that Sir Roger Woddis, who
was i/c our mob's entire intelligence operation for years and years,
was all along drawing his pay cheque from the Moscow-Narodny
Bank left in a hole in a tree in Green Park every Friday night.
(Boris was a bit cagey about whether this was true, but I told
him I wouldn't be in the least bit surprised, as all those FO people
were shirtlifters and Commies at one time or another.)

News eventually trickles back to the UK: Boss very incensed
about disloyalty, re-run of Cheltenham GCHQ lark, 007 Johnny
signed name in blood, crossed his heart and swore to die etc.
Next thing is she's on the blower to poor old Havers, who finds
himself called out of the Garrick Club at half past four in the

afternoon, and our friend Sir Robert Armstrong, the bottom-pincher behind the green baize door (see my last) is dispatched c.o.d. on Qantas with a briefcase full of writs, injunctions etc all tied up in red tape, and calculated to put the fear of God into the beer-swilling Colonial pettifoggers.

I could have warned them in advance that this was pissing in the wind in no uncertain manner. These Anzacs have very little time for discipline, as you may remember when Prosser-Cluff called a Clap Parade outside the garrison chapel at Kuala Lumpur and Ozzie Woodnutt set fire to his bed in retaliation.

Armstrong duly arrives in Oz and here, according to Boris, the plot thickens somewhat. Counsel for the Defence pointed out that this Woddis story had already appeared several years ago and was all old hat. It transpired that some Branestawm figure called Rothschild with connections in the City who was brought in by Heath to run his Think Tank had previously introduced Brother Wright to one Chapman Pinscher, a former reptile, with a view to bringing the story before a wider public.

Why, I hear you enquire, should Rothschild, this supposedly brilliant egghead, go to such lengths to expose the fact that our nation's intelligence service had been working for the other side? Something of an own goal, you might opine. I confessed to Boris that I was totally foxed, even given the fact that all these University people have a tendency to instability and getting the wrong end of the stick. Boris, equally baffled in my view, produced a very far-fetched theory that Rothschild, who, he told me, had invented invisible ink while working for MI5 during the war, was laying down smoke to distract attention from his own weekly pay cheque from the Narodny Bank, which would go some way to explain his life-style and love of fine wines. (This last bit is entre nous, I need hardly say, so please don't breathe a word in the Merry Leper.)

So much for the Defence.

Meanwhile Friend Havers, who had been having another heavy lunch with his cronies, gets very maudlin about his name being taken in vain in the Ozzie courtroom, and finds his way 'unsteady with grief' to make a personal complaint to the Boss, demanding an apology, costs and damages for a disgraceful imputation, i.e. that he had suggested prosecuting the 007 cove in the first place. I took the liberty of lingering outside the sanctum after he had shuffled in and could recognise the delightful sound of Hurricane Maggie centring on some other area than the back of my own neck. Did he know the meaning of the term 'gibbering idiot'? First Westland and now this. If he thought that he was going to get Pegleg Hailsham's perch on the Woolsack he was gravely mistaken. And in future when he came round she'd be obliged if he'd gargle with TCP as she had quite enough of being breathed over in that manner in the privacy of her own home. I thought it prudent at this point to tiptoe away, but I could hear Havers sobbing most affectingly. Actually I'd take all that with a largish pinch of salt as these lawyer swine are very skilled at putting on that kind of an act when it suits their book. We passed later in the afternoon in the doorway of a little club I sometimes toddle into in Old Compton Street and he looked straight through me, grinning all over his face.

Could I rely on you to pick up the hamper that Maurice has ordered for our Boxing Day Old Lags' Match at Huntercombe? Knowing Maurice there'll be something to pay, despite the fact that it was brought in in the Diplomatic Bag from Taiwan. Mum's the word.

DENIS

10 Downing Street
Whitehall

26 DECEMBER 1986

Dear Bill,

What ghastly news about your leg. I've always said the revolving door at the RAC was highly dangerous, especially after lunch, and now your accident has proved it. I couldn't quite follow from your call in the Casualty Department who was carrying who, but I'm sure you have a case in law, and I'm told there's a very good little man called Carter Ruck who will put the fear of God into that Club Secretary, given a reasonable sweetener in advance.

Talking of Yuletide jollity, you didn't miss anything not coming to M's beano in honour of Van der Pump's four score years. Prince Bigears honoured us with his presence, minus that coathanger wife of his, and there were a lot of weirdoes from the world of headshrinking, as well as some very bewildered friends of Mrs Van der Kafferbesher with big estates in the Transvaal. A plastic barrel of South African sherry didn't exactly set the party on a roar and I got stuck in a corner with some extremely odd woman with hairy legs and open-toed sandals who told me all about her dreams. At some point HRH called for a bit of hush and read out a poem written on bark which had been sent to him by a Bushman in honour of Old Chief Bald Springbok, which is apparently how they think of him in those parts. Van der P. then made a gracious response, comparing the Boss to some fertility goddess or other called Moo who is credited with increasing the GNP of Rumbabaland by a thousand-fold in days gone by. He then broke into song, accompanying himself on a goatskin drum, at which moment I gathered up a few dirty plastic cups and beat it into the pantry where Boris was waiting with a Knockout Ukrainian Lifesaver.

Have you been following this radar business in the *Telegraph*? M. and Co. were in a bit of a quandary as per usual about Backing Britain v. Something Cheaper that Actually Works, and the Boss after all the whirlibirds trouble last Christmas with Heseltine and little Brittan was decidedly uncertain which side of the fence to come down on. The matter was settled by old Fatty Prior. I don't know whether you remember him. He used to open the bowling for the Wets' Eleven and finally got ten years hard in Ulster for answering back in Cabinet. Not a bad egg, but no idea how to handle Margaret. Anyway, on getting the bird from M's lot he was offered a very cushy number as chairman of GEC, a big electrics outfit with prestige offices in Mayfair run by a wily little Johnny called Weinberger or Beefstock or something of that nature. This geezer foolishly thought that it would assist his operation no end to pick up discarded Cabinet Ministers and put their names on his writing paper. The first to benefit from his largesse was Peter Carrington who you remember did the decent thing when the balloon went up in the Falklands. Then Peter landed one of these plum jobs in Brussels stuffing his face with pate de foie gras with American generals, so Weintraub snapped up Fatty to fill the gap. Slightly larger armchair in the boardroom, otherwise business as before.

However I could have told him that the sight of Farmer Jim's name on the promotional material for the Nimrod Flying Dustbin would be like a red rag to a bull as far as M. was concerned. Sure enough, no sooner had Fatty made a rousing speech in favour

'. . . I got stuck in a corner with some extremely
odd woman . . .'

of buying British that M. was on the blower to the Awacs office in New York giving them the glad tidings.

What did I tell you? A couple of weeks back I hinted that that bearded sidekick of Runcie's was up to no good in the Middle East. Not for a moment was I deceived by his Holy Joe act dispensing peace and light outside the sordid world of politics. Now of course it turns out that he was a mere dupe of Hopalong's shuffling to and fro with a small-arms catalogue concealed in the false bottom of his overnight bag. If you ask me the next thing we'll be told is that Runcie is actually up to his neck in the whole business, wheeling and dealing away with his Brother in God the Ayatollah Khomeini.

Re Boxing Day. If you and Maurice would be prepared to spring me we'll fill up at the Waggonload of Monkeys and then tootle over to Huntercombe with a view to getting well and truly plastered by nightfall.

Has Maurice sent you his Christmas card yet? I thought his Air Malta lady posing on the bar in her flamenco costume hardly suitable to the religious spirit of Christmastide, and the verse written in mine even less so:

> Bottoms up, my dear old friend
> Care to pull this Cracker?
> If Yuletide Fun you should intend
> She's yours for Half a Smacker.

Yours incorrigibly,

DENIS

10 Downing Street
Whitehall

Dear Bill,

I can't apologise enough for your embarrassment on Boxing Day. Neither the guards on the perimeter fence nor their dogs are in any way under my control and I have offered to pay for a new pair of golfing trousers for Maurice. I'm glad to hear that his Air Malta lady came to the rescue with a pair of kilt pins, but it must have been a very disagreeable experience ordering drinks at Huntercombe.

As I explained over the phone to Maurice, our Escape Plan was aborted at the last minute. I had assumed that my attendance on Christmas Day at an atrocious gathering of Margaret's choice would qualify me for at least a day's R & R on compassionate grounds. Not so. Do you remember that awful creep Parkinson with the slicked down hair who blotted his copy book with some tea-lady at the Ministry? (My memory of these things is becoming confused.) Ever since he was given the bum's rush, the Boss has kept a photograph of him on her desk alongside Hopalong riding Trigger and has meanwhile taken to muttering his name late at night. Oystereyes and the sounder element have told her over and over again that she's well shot of the slippery little bugger but Margaret froths at the mouth at any word of criticism and still insists that Smarmy Cecil was the best thing since power-assisted corkscrews.

Naturally it's none of my business what they do at Number Ten, but I did blow a gasket when the Old Girl announced unilaterally over the lightly-boiled on Christmas Eve that Mr and Mrs P. were to be guests of honour at our festive luncheon. I said Christmas was surely bad enough without that randy little ferret getting his whiskers in the brandy butter, whereupon storm cones were hoisted and I got ten minutes of Yuletide being the time for reconciliation and forgiveness, followed by a lot of gush, presumably culled from Van der Pump, about bushfolk embracing scapegoats. Never one to fly the field at such a juncture, I took a slug of Boris's electric soup, and said 'goat' was plum

'. . . and a pair of red frilly knickers fluttered onto the table . . .'

on the nose and I didn't want this particular specimen sniffing round the RAF ladies at Chequers during drinking hours.

Needless to say force majeure prevailed and I resigned myself to the presence of the socially mobile Cecil, complete with put-upon wife.

I think Boris may have overdone it with the pre-lunch stiffeners, as I noticed both M. and Mrs P. shoot me a pretty rum look when I wielded the carving knife aloft and enquired whether Cecil fancied a bit of breast or was he a leg man? Mr Wu, who was ladling out the bread sauce, let out a high-pitched titter at this point, repeating 'Bleast or Leg! Ha ha ha ho ho ho!' and spilt a goodly dollop down the back of Mrs Parkinson's dress, producing the inevitable laser beam from the other end of the table.

After which things quietened down for a bit. Come Sticky Time however, when everyone had had a few, Mr P's eye alighted on the crackers and turning with a deferential leer to the Prime Minister, he cried, 'Margaret, you and I must pull together as we have so often in the past!' 'Bravo, Cecil!' enthused the Boss, her face flushed with the unaccustomed sticky, 'Well spoken!' At this she grasped the crepe paper and gave a heave. There was a sharp crack and a pair of red frilly knickers fluttered onto the table. It transpired that Mr Wu had very foolishly distributed Maurice's Old Compton Street Surprise Selection instead of the ones M. had ordered from Fortnum's. This denouement was too much for our Oriental major domo, who fell through the service door shouting 'Led Knickers!' over and over again until brought to his senses by Boris slapping him round the face.

Worse was to come. The following morning I was just examining my somewhat sallow complexion in the bathroom mirror prior to slipping into the golfing togs when the Boss threw open the door without knocking and announced that I was to be in the drawing room sober at half past twelve as we had an important guest. Jeffrey Archer had very sweetly rung to wish her a Happy Christmas, and wouldn't it be a lovely idea to ask him over? Before I had time to answer she slammed the door. I was still speechless when Boris came in with his Princess Dracula pick-me-up, a recipe passed down by Vlad the Impaler, and informed me that the Archer lark was all a scheme of the Saatchis to burnish up the Boss's image as a compassionate and loyal woman who was prepared to let bygones be bygones. I said it wasn't very compassionate towards me, let alone loyal, and as with Cecil P., loyalty and compassion didn't come into it, she actually liked the little buggers wriggling their buttocks round the place and laying on the charm with a loaded trowel. Mercifully the Archer Experience passed me by in a haze of blurred colours and oddly distorted voices and I woke up twenty-four hours later behind the sofa in the TV room.

Did you see that old Snaggleteeth Macmillan finally turned his toes up? There were a lot of crocodile tears shed in this neck of the woods, as he was a thorn in the flesh as far as the Boss was concerned, always tottering up to put the boot in with effortless old-world charm. Incidentally, I was told by a friend of O'Gooley's who worked at the hospital for Distressed Officers that Supermac was played a very nasty trick by the medical fraternity. When he went sick in 1963 the saw-bones on duty shook his head and told him he was a goner. The Old Walrus accordingly handed in his cards as P.M., gave the job to his school-chum Skull-face Home whereupon they open him up and there's nothing wrong with him bar a bit of Old Men's Waterworks trouble, just like the Major. Rest of his life he was fit as a fiddle, and very, very cross. Moral: never believe a word the medics tell you.

Anyway, there's no chance of the Boss throwing in the towel

prematurely and I heard her telling Alberto Saatchi the other day that given the present mood in the City she should be sitting pretty till A D 2018. I suppose you don't know anyone who'd be interested in renting Dulwich? What about that couple we met in Portugal with the Rotweilers? Whittam-Smith? Prendergast? Weren't they looking for five bedrooms, three reception rooms near a golf course?

The Mermaid is inked in. Bring your new Japanese putters and the Highballs will be on me, as the Giraffe said to the Warthog.

Yrs in anticipation,

DENIS

10 Downing Street
Whitehall

23 JANUARY 1987

Dear Bill,

Did you see me on the Box going backstage at the Royal Opera House? Crikey, the things one goes through in the cause of marital harmony and a third term! Apparently some of those wretched punters were not only there voluntarily but had actually paid two hundred nicker to struggle through the ice and snow from Golders Green for four hours of Eyetie caterwauling in that over-upholstered clip joint. Talking of Icecreamios, I understand it was our friends Alberto y Luigi di Saatchi who were behind it all. Alberto pointed out that M. had had far too much exposure at the B2/C2 end of the market, doing damnfool phone-ins and chewing the fat with that miserable little geriatric ex-pop singer in the toupee on Radio Two, Jimmy Whatsisname. So the order went out that it was time for the After Eights mints slot.

Hence my reluctant presence at the back of the Royal Box on Tuesday night. Luckily Boris had taken the precaution of treble-starching my shirt-front to preserve the appearance of alert interest. I myself had filled my Queen Mother Emergency Gusset

'. . . going backstage at the Royal Opera House . . .'

Tank with high-octane antifreeze, so I missed one or two of the quieter scenes. But it seemed to me a pretty bloody stupid story. Some overweight Coon big-shot strangles his wife in a mix-up over his European ADC's hanky. The girl herself, who's a perfectly ordinary Italian without so much as a touch of the tarbrush, is obviously a bit of a drop-out or she wouldn't have got mixed up with a native. It all goes to show that Van der Pump's lot are basically sound about keeping the races firmly apart. If this message is hammered well and truly home then perhaps there is some sense in pouring money into that Palais de Snobs after all. When we went backstage I said as much to Sir Claus Moser, who tears the tickets, and I must say he gave me a very fishy look.

How are you coping with the arctic conditions down in Kent? I understand Maurice was out in his Snow Rover flogging off a consignment of Japanese hairdryers for unfreezing waterpipes and got stuck on the Maidstone by-pass. When the emergency services finally reached him he was paralytic, got breathalysed trying to reverse out of the snow-drift and spent the night in chokey. Meanwhile Margaret was having to put up with a lot of flak from the Wets about helping the Wrinklies out with their heating bills and there was a hurried U-turn about letting them have the cash even though the temperature hadn't reached the statutory 100 degrees-below previously enforced by M. Maurice rang before his accident in very vocal mood, to say that it was their own lookout if they wouldn't install double-glazing and why didn't the Government pay the subsidy direct to Picwarmth? I passed this on to Fowler, but he's far too busy wasting money on these Cecil B. de Mille commercials for AIDS. I haven't had my leaflet yet because the post has ground to a halt, but Whitelaw tells me the message is to keep a packet of Featherlite handy whenever you go out to dinner. It's come to something when Nanny State has to lecture the young on things you and I had to work out for ourselves. The vital message they ought to be putting across, i.e. that when you sup with a shirtlifter you should use a very long spoon, is left to the small print, but that's because 99.9% of all Civil Servants are of that persuasion and don't want to draw attention to themselves.

You see Runcie's Undercover Arms-dealer with the Beard is off on his travels again? He's obviously up to something pretty murky. An innocent Frog photographer took his picture, and immediately had a bag thrown over his head and was whisked off, never to be seen again. Personally I can't wait for him to be hauled before one of these Yank Committees and asked to spill the beans by a lot of Senators with microphones. Quite honestly this Angel of Mercy in a Beard act is fooling no one at all and little old ladies in the C of E putting their money in the plate really don't want it spent on poolside drinks for Beardy and Friends in the Beirut Hilton.

I asked Furniss about the BA sell-off and he says it isn't intended to recruit any more Sids, i.e. mug any more people into voting Tory, so after all it might be worth risking a pony. Lawson who I asked about it when he was wiping the snow off the back of his Volvo outside Number Eleven said, 'It wouldn't really interest you, Denis, it's only for the Big Boys.' Condescending little prat! Little does he know that I could write a cheque for the whole of BA and not know I'd done it.

I got a very funny letter from the man at the Mermaid. Have you any recollection of Maurice pushing a halbert, whatever that is, through the ceiling? I suppose it could have happened after you and I and the Major had toddled up the wooden hill to Bedfordshire. I formed the impression that he and that American widow lady intended to make a night of it, but I certainly heard nothing untoward. He's asking for £750 plus VAT.

If you do manage to struggle up to town I could give you lunch at the RAC and we could do the Lillywhite's sale in the afternoon. Japanese Moon Boots are down to £199.99 and they've got freezer bags for the caddy to carry with your clubs that take three litres of gin, one of tonic, and a compartment full of ice cubes in the form of golf balls. Sounds rather amusing. I hope it goes better than Gieves & Hawkes. They were flogging off a suit of mine that I'd sent back and it was torn into fifteen pieces within moments of the shop doors being opened.

Your old Brass Monkey chum,

DENIS

10 Downing Street
Whitehall

6 FEBRUARY 1987

Dear Bill,

It seems only yesterday that I was writing to you, confidently looking forward to a few declining years of golden twilight to be whiled away down in Dulwich in the cool of my insulated alcohol store. Then, as you may recall, that idiot Michael Foot ensured a walk-over at the last election and it was back to the Iron Mask routine for a second term. Now it looks horribly as though history may be about to repeat itself. The stupid freckled prat Kinnock has had ninety-one shots at the undefended goal from ten feet and rooted it into the crowd at every single bloody attempt.

Personally I blame that wife of his. It's perfectly obvious that she wears the trousers, and Boris tells me that all this CND stuff is entirely her idea. Poor little Pillock gets his marching orders while he's still groggy before breakfast and cold tongue pie when he gets home in the evenings if he hasn't delivered the goods. Just imagine me propped up on one elbow in bed lecturing the Boss on Foreign Affairs at four o'clock in the morning when she wants a bit of shut-eye. Short shrift is an inadequate description of what I would receive.

The latest balls-up by our lot concerns some kind of Sputnik device dreamed up by the boffins which will fly very low over Moscow every fifteen minutes whipping Mrs Gorbachov's washing off the line and generally spreading havoc and despondency among the Comrades. Some ghastly little Communist ex-student working for a rag read by about four disgruntled members of the pipe-and-sandals brigade strolls in, bold as brass and makes a film about it for the BBC. Lights, cameras, action, megaphones – the only people who don't know about it, apparently, is HMG.

This of course only confirms what I've always said about the BBC being a nest of pinko vipers funded directly by the Kremlin. And if that little greaser Milne thinks he's going to get a knighthood while I have any say in the matter he can damn well think again.

When the Boss eventually found out, every fuse in the box burst into flames. Shades of GCHQ, Pinko Ponting and that awful man in Australia with the corks dangling from his hat. No wonder we were a laughing stock, I heard her screaming at Howe, when we couldn't keep anything secret for five minutes without the enemy being handed it all on a plate by some grubby little man with a chip on his shoulder.

Next thing, Havers is hauled out of the Garrick all over again at four o'clock in the afternoon in a pretty comatose state, to slap writs and injunctions on all and sundry. A bit silly after it had already been in the papers, just like when that FO Johnny shot his mouth off very soundly about the Wogs a few weeks back. Meanwhile a couple of charabanc loads of Old Bill are dispatched to kick down the door of Comrade Mole's malodorous bed-sitter taking away socks etc for forensic analysis. Surprise, surprise – it transpires from correspondence lying round the place that Havers knew about the film all along and had doubtless been chuckling over it with the various actor laddies and stage-door wooftahs that constitute the membership of that particular club of his.

Once more the Kinnock Penalty with all Margaret's team clutching their balls at the wrong end of the field. Will the boyo slam it in the net? Will he hell. The Dulwich Eventide rainbow fades again.

The only good news to have come out of the whole ghastly balls-up is that Peg-Leg 'The Duke' Hussey, one of the heavies Margaret sent round to measure up the Pinkoes at the BBC for concrete overcoats, has finally taken his tommy-gun out of the cello case and rubbed out little Milne, who was supposed to be i/c the Nest of Trots. Margaret was very pleased when the news came through about the bloodbath, and rang up Peg-Leg to tell him to move in 'one of ours' as soon as the chalk marks had been washed off the floor. Not as easy as it sounds, if you ask me. What they need is someone like Prosser-Cluff who would go in there and sort the buggers out with a baseball bat, but you don't find that calibre of management at Shepherd's Bush. However, hats off to the Glasgow Police for raiding the studio and letting them know they're not a no-go area.

Most of last week the Boss was on the blower to Snaggleteeth Runcie asking what had become of 'that dear, sweet Mr Waite', lost in the labyrinth of wartorn Beirut. Did Runcie fully under-stand what would happen to him if a hair of his dear beard was harmed? According to Boris she's not fooling anyone and knows perfectly well that Runcie can do sod all about it.

'. . . Van der Pump is scattering his little bag of chicken bones on the carpet . . .'

Have you been following the trial of that old bag the self-styled Madame Sin of Tooting Bec? Maurice rang up in some consternation, claiming that he'd been there innocently distributing his Timeshare brochures when the Boys in Blue had come tumbling in. Could I have a word with Havers about keeping his name out of it as his Air Malta lady was suffering from depression and her doctors said that any publicity of this kind could precipitate a crisis. I told him to get in touch with this little fellow Carter Ruck I recommended when you had that trouble with the swing door at the RAC. I made the same suggestion to Munster, whose name had been blackened by some bespectacled windbag on the *Guardian* who quoted him as saying that no one with a conscience votes for our lot. (Entre nous, a perfectly sensible remark, but you can't have the Smellisocks trumpeting it around the place when there's an election coming up.) Just when I can't exactly tell you, but the Corsican Twins are closeted with M. even as I write and Van der Pump is scattering his little bag of chicken bones on the carpet. Where will it all end?

Yours in the rough,

DENIS

10 Downing Street
Whitehall
20 FEBRUARY 1987

Dear Bill,

Thank God that's all over, as I said to the man at Moss Bros when I took my kit back after the boy Mark's wedding. He said he wouldn't be too sure about that these days. People thought nothing of having a second bite of the cherry after they found a maggot in the first one. Half the geezers queueing in there, he said, were on their second or third marriages and in his opinion some folks never learned. Fortunately he was so busy talking he didn't spot the hole burned in the seat of the trousers where I sat on old Buggerdorfer's stogie, which he foolishly left smouldering on the arm of a chaise longue in the American bar.

Incidentally I'd no idea the Savoy had its own chapel. I suppose it's a bit like Harrods having their own mortuary – a lot of Americans pegging out after overdoing it in the Grill. It's all done up to look very antique, and has the huge advantage over other Godboxes of being so small it didn't cause old Buggerdorfer to reach too deep into his back pocket. As I explained to him in the line-up, he could count himself damn lucky there wasn't more room, otherwise he'd have had every wino and freeloader from Halitosis Hall and most of Fleet Street getting their snouts in the trough at his expense.

Boss bore up very well under the circs. I didn't say anything to her about it, but between the two of us I think she may have felt a bit let down by the son and heir fetching up with the daughter of a used car dealer. After all that trouble with her elocution lessons and so forth and sending the little bugger to Harrow I think she may secretly have entertained ideas of his bagging the daughter of a duke, like David Frost and Lady Ocarina. Personally I think he should count himself damn lucky. Any presentable woman who is prepared to take him on for better or worse, mostly worse if my experience is anything to go by, has my profound gratitude.

Maurice had sent me something called the *Best Man's Book of Wedding Jokes*, and I confess I burned the midnight oil the night before, having no end of a chuckle as I composed a few quips to set the assembled Yankee knucklebrains on a roar. In the cold light of day, however, under Margaret's steely gaze, I decided that some of the riper chestnuts were better discarded. However, come the off, and emboldened by a goodly scoop or twain of Buggerdorfer's Californian bubbly, discretion went to the winds and I told the story about the Major's honeymoon in Bruges when they both got taken away on the same stretcher. The U.S. contingent seemed to enjoy this story insofar as they understood it but I was aware of the gamma rays behind me dispersing the clouds of alcoholic bonhomie. Foolishly perhaps, I pressed on, drawing a parallel between the boy Mark and some of the rusty heaps of metal on sale at Buggerdorfer's Used Car Emporium in Downtown Dallas. Nothing on the clock that couldn't be put right with an electric drill, only one previous owner (this got the biggest laugh of the afternoon), bit of a gas guzzler perhaps, but nonetheless a conversation piece. I remember finding this amazingly funny at the time. However, when I sat down to moderate applause and turned to Margaret for approval I could see that she was in the grip of powerful emotions and

b.

'. . . I told the story about the Major's honeymoon . . .'

that any immediate attempt to return to the hearth and home would be ill-judged. I therefore sloped off with Charlie Whackett, who had after all very decently fixed the whole thing in the first place, and as I recall finished up in the small hours somewhere in Tooting where Charlie is trying to build a few more of his multi-storey car parks.

Talking of that sort of thing, you will be pleased to hear that the Boss has given the green light to 'resuscitating the rural economy', very much along the lines I proposed some years back with my Sunshine Homes in Snowdonia scheme which ran into a bit of difficulty at the time. As you and I know, the woolly hatted bird-watching weirdoes and Greenpeace freaks have had it their own way for far too long and nowadays you can't even cut a tree down without being taken to court by a lot of muesli addicts masquerading as some kind of Preservation Society. I was talking to the Barratts man down at Dulwich and he reckons there are plum sites all over the Home Counties where anyone with an ear to the ground and a working knowledge of which palms to grease can really clean up. Maurice has got his eye on some prime land round the M25 for Green Belt Leisure Centres with in-house hypermarket facilities and fully-motorised golf courses.

I hope you took my advice and plonked a wodge of brown ones on the BA shares. Furniss reckons I've cleaned up to the tune of several thou. and thank goodness they didn't let the yobboes in on this one as a Tory Party recruiting gimmick. If I had any doubts about the wisdom of taking a quick profit, seeing that prize Charlie with the glasses and the silly face M's put in to run it pretty soon dispelled them.

I imagine it was you who sent that Valentine Card to the Boss with the pop-up effect and musical accompaniment. I'm sorry to say that Boris inadvertently de-activated it with his metal detector, so some of the humour was lost on opening the envelope.

See you at Worplesdon on the 20th. I'll bring what's left of poor old Buggerdorfer's Champers in the boot of the Roller.

Yours tearfully,

DENIS

10 Downing Street
Whitehall

6 MARCH 1987

Dear Bill,

Thank you for your brochure for the Algarve Package. Personally I am reluctant to abandon Mother Flack in favour of this new Al Badawi Golfotel, of which I notice they only furnish an artist's impression suggesting that there's probably not much more than a hole in the ground and a notice board. I entirely agree that the Widow Flack's hollow legs may have sprung a leak or two in her old age and that the service is at times slowed down by her amnesia and 'fainting fits', but there is such a thing as loyalty, and fifty pee for a large G and T must still be the best value in the Common Market.

As far as any forward planning is concerned, I am in my usual difficulties. You probably saw the Boss posing with a basket of Ugly Fruit before dawn in some Northern hell-hole, loudly proclaiming to the bemused costers that an election was the last thing she was thinking of. But nearer home I can tell you the talk is of little else. Hardly a day passes without Tebbit and the Corsicans coming round with graphs and market research material trying to pin-point the top of the curve.

In view of what happened last time I hesitate to ask her point blank how she feels about me swanning off to points south for two weeks' well-merited R & R at, say, the end of June. As things stand, particularly with our Mr Wimpo down at Greenwich limping in just ahead of the Monster Raving Loonies' Dirty Macintosh Party, I don't myself see her applying the match to the blue touch paper before the leaves are on the trees, but a lot will depend on Matey Next Door, for whom things would appear to be very much coming up roses, judging at least from his smug smile as he squeezes himself behind the wheel of his Volvo and shouts his usual innuendo of inebriation at Yours Truly as I set out for my constitutional.

According to Furniss at the NatWest, they've got so much money in the vaults now that they can afford to knock half a per cent off interest rates and still be wallowing in champagne come Christmas, so he reckoned Fatso will take tuppence off the Income Tax, deluge the OAPs in free condoms and go to the country on a wave of patriotic euphoria bang after the Budget.

Things do not seem so simple from this end of the bar, however, where in addition to the aforementioned sages Saatchi, Saatchi and Tebbit, we rely heavily on the oracular pronouncements of Margaret's wild-eyed soothsayer Van der P. with his little bag of goats' bones and dried entrails. Apparently he has solemnly assured M. that during his upcoming hike through the Kalahari with Prince Bigears, he will consult the Whistling Hole of Mbobo, down which suppliants traditionally throw their loincloths in exchange for useful tips.

Poor old Hoppo, as you may have seen on the TV, seems to be moving peacefully towards his close. The trouble with the Yanks is that they will insist on poring over the dirty laundry for hours and hours in the full glare of the flash bulbs, with the result they all end up with pretty red faces. Questioned about this Irangate caper, Hoppo kicked off with a line about not being able to remember anything, then he said he had remembered

'. . . saying he was going to join the Papists . . .'

and forgotten again, now he says he can remember forgetting it very clearly but can't remember what it was he forgot. Boris says the country is being run by the Emaciated Spouse, which is pretty grisly news for mankind (as the man said when he found there was no booze on the moon), Mrs R. having an IQ slightly lower than that of the average cocker spaniel. Just imagine what would happen if the Boss suddenly went down with a nasty dose of Altzheimer's, couldn't remember where the bathroom was, and yours truly had to stand up at Question Time and take a lot of cheek from the Smellisocks. Doesn't really bear thinking about.

You might think, incidentally, that Margaret would be feeling a bit sorry for the poor old cowboy, but when I raised the question during the Happy Hour the matronly eye remained as cold as that of a fish on a slab. One thing that may have contributed to this is the revelation, perfectly obvious to everyone at the time, that Hoppo's lightning strike on Libya was targeted on Brer Gadaffi in person as he sat in his tent reading the *Radio Times*. Of course he didn't tell her that when it was happening or she might have had rather cold feet about letting them do it from Somewhere in East Anglia. If you ask me, the silver-framed photograph on the drinks cabinet may soon join that of Peter Carrington on top of the wardrobe.

Did you see that little prat Gummer posing in the *Telegraph* saying he was going to join the Papists if they let in women priests? I think even the Pope might draw the line at having J. Selwyn G. aboard. My only consolation is that by the time the Vicarettes take over I shall be under the sod. Talking of which, Runcie has a lot to answer for. You don't think he's actually a woman himself, do you? That's Maurice's theory. There's certainly something very odd about the way he walks.

Pax vobiscum,

DENIS

10 Downing Street
Whitehall

20 MARCH 1987

Dear Bill,

By the time you read this, Mr Fatso from Number Eleven will have opened his battered old lunchbox and showered the punters with used fivers. After all the leaking that's been going on, security at this end has been tightened up, so I couldn't have given you chapter and verse in any case. But, as you will by now have gathered, no palm has been left ungreased, fountains are flowing with G and T, general euphoria. Mark my words they'll be into the starting gates before you can say Robinson's Golliwog Marmalade.

However, long before Matey next door stood up to read out the good news about his Giveaway Everything Must Go Spring Sale, Mr Munster and the Wizards of the own goal on the Smelli-socks side had ensured that the Corsicans had smiles playing about their jaundiced lips. Little Pillock had only just emerged in his Scourge of the Hard Left Costume when up pops old Farmer Jim Callaghan to put the muddy boot in. You may remember last time there was an election he ploughed up the green just as Gingernuts was making his final putt, telling them they were daft to go naked into the Conference Chamber with the Bear. Sure enough, scenting that his Leader was again poised over the putter, up he pops on his earthmover, shouting the odds about Trident.

Questioned by that honking-voiced piss-artist on the wireless with the bow-tie, Pillock declares that the Elder Statesman is an enfeebled anachronism with one foot in the grave, whose views are of no interest as he is too gaga even to stand without assistance in the next election. However, scarcely has the spit dried on the microphone than ugly scenes occur in the so-called House of Commons Tea Room, i.e. Afternoon Drinking Club. In the hearing of many of our fruitier members from the Shires, one of Pillock's Left Hand Men called Prescott strides up to the Old Farmer, bold as brass, and shouts out, 'You bastard, you've screwed it up again' – or words to that effect, I haven't got Hansard to hand – at which the former Able Seaman hollers,

'. . . interviewed by that honking-voiced piss-artist . . .'

'Don't talk to me like that, Sonny Boy! If you'd listened to me before, you wouldn't be up shit creek today!' Again I paraphrase in the absence of the official communique. Fisticuffs are narrowly averted. Prescott dragged away by the Yobs, rubicund old gentlemen of our persuasion scamper downstairs to the phones to tell the reptiles all about it.

Next morning, poor Pillock leaves home spruce and neat to announce his manifesto for creating two million new jobs overnight, this being his trump card, only to find a caravanserai of hacks camping on the pavement seeking his views on last night's Big Fight. There are times when I almost feel sorry for the little man. Very hard on him having such a bossy wife. Now he's developed a persecution mania about the newspapers being beastly to him and spends all his time going through the *Star* with a magic marker underlining instances of bias.

In the light of all this, I took little Mr Rosenthal of Giddier and Giddier my estate agents out to lunch with a view to putting Dulwich back on the market. I did so with a heavy heart, having spent all that money on the thermostatically controlled alcohol store, but it seems a bit pointless hanging on to it when one is clearly destined to drop in harness. Rosenthal said that after this Budget house prices are going to be through the stratosphere so I should sit tight for the immediate future, but he's got a very nice South African on the hook, who turns out to be related to the Van der Kafferbeshers and clearly has his finger in the wind. (Incidentally Mrs Van der K. herself has gone pretty quiet of late, no doubt busy building her fall-out shelter.)

Munster got his arse rather badly chewed last week over this Oxford Chancellorship farrago. The story went the rounds that he was organising a Vote for Heath Campaign in order to stop that old SDP wino from getting to hand out the Latin Book Tokens on Speech Day, thus notching up another victory for the Alliance. The word had soon reached the opium dens of Fleet Street that this was a directive from Number Ten, and within moments Munster was tapping on the Boss's door. From what I could hear, he was harshly rebuked. Party politics, she cried, did not come into this. Mr Jenkins was a distinguished academic and historian with a fine knowledge of wine and a reputation throughout the drawing rooms of Europe. The other candidates were an obscure port-addict from the Queen's College and half a ton of condemned meat in a suit. (Guess who?)

See you at Worplesdon. Did you see those Italian friends of Maurice's from Woking got put away for life? I had no idea they were in the Mafia.

DENIS

 10 Downing Street
Whitehall

3 APRIL 1987

Dear Bill,
At last a ray of hope! According to the Corsican Twins, Alberto y Luigi, there is now a good chance that the struck-off GP in the suit and his little Scottish friend will come up from behind in the last few furlongs, thus depriving the Old Girl of her Silver Jubilee. Meanwhile Mr Munster has been helping things forward. Off his own bat he set up various press conferences to rubbish Batman and Robin who he described as 'Socialists'. This produced

a few laughs. Even I could have told him that the Doctor was about as Socialist as the Major's brother. I always remember the time he tried to strangle that Trot at Brighton for pelting him with over-ripe fruit (the Doctor, I mean, not the Major's brother, although he went in for a good deal of that kind of thing. Wasn't he up for GBH after an altercation with a lady bus conductor?)

Net result of Munster's intervention was to boost the Doc a good half-dozen points in the Polls, public sympathy always attaching to anyone into the seat of whose trousers Brer Tebbit locks his incisors. Munster was carpeted, and as usual got very emotional, accusing the Boss of seeing Cecil behind his back, which, entre nous, is perfectly true. Boris tells me they meet in a parked car in the Horse Guards' Parade. Not that it's any skin off my nose, but if I was Munster I might well feel the rug was on the verge of being twitched. As you know, Norman's never been exactly Number One on my hit parade, but when it comes to Cecil we see eye to eye. I even offered him a slug of electric soup as he slunk out last time and let him sit in the den until he got over his weeping fit. Now the Saatchis have sent him off to a charm school in Surrey to soften his polecat image on the TV. Money down the drain in my opinion.

A stroke of luck, being excused boots over the Moscow outing. I was all teed up to go and Boris had provided me with a map of the inner city with off-licences ringed in red where one can get a bottle under the counter in exchange for hard currency. But then some little smart-arse from MI5 tootled round and denounced me to the Boss as a Grade One Security Risk, painting a vivid picture of Yours Truly, having taken a skinful, being lured into some back room by a busty Aeroflot hostess who would scissor through one's braces and hurl one on the floor in a compromising clinch. I ask you, Bill. I've been on these outings before and you're jolly lucky if you're let off the leash to walk the length of a hotel corridor without being jumped on by one of our heavies.

Coincidentally, it seems, the Saatchis outlined to Margaret the handicap I'd be in any kind of mixed doubles, when the glamorous Mrs Gorblimov would score useful points ranged against a decrepit old wino like myself. Upshot anyhow was three days of golf at St Andrews, marred only by Maurice P. keeling over on the fourteenth and having to be given the kiss of life by a little man in a kilt who happened to be passing. I must say my

'. . . Maurice P. keeling over on the fourteenth . . .'

heart went out to Gorblimov getting all that nagging from the Boss. Imagine what you'd feel like if some old bat with a shopping bag came in and sat in your office and lectured you in Russian for hours on end about civil rights.

Poor little Pillock scored another own goal by not checking Margaret's diary and flew off for a ten-minute fireside chat with Hopalong, squeezed between the Venezuelan Ambassador and a delegation of Mormons from Salt Lake City. Naturally his presence went unnoticed by the media, those not covering Margaret's Moscow Nights being hot on the trail of that ghastly *Dynasty* slag and her alimony-grabbing Swedish dentist.

I continue to be rather touched by Pillock's plight. The reptiles are always so beastly to him, and now the black Trots are after his blood for not letting them set up an Apartheid system in the Labour Party. I think if I were him I'd chuck it all in and open a nice little Welsh tea-room on the borders, where there are always quite a lot of trippers who'd be perfectly happy to listen to his colourful Welsh reminiscences. It would certainly be preferable to shouting into Hoppo's hearing aid in the certain knowledge he has no idea who you are, with Old Panda-features Healey nudging you in the ribs every time you get your lines wrong. I expect it's only his wife who keeps him at it.

Thank you for your amusing postcard about King Faht's visit. His name is not pronounced like that but the photo was very entertaining all the same. We had them all round for lunch as per usual and I was given a mashie made of solid gold with my name picked out in diamonds on the handle. No bloody use for hitting a ball with, needless to say, and since that chappie got caught out with a teapot we have to hand everything over to the Ministry of Works to be melted down and put towards the National Debt. I got in a word to Fatso about Maurice's car-phone scheme, and he gave me the name of the man you have to send the money to in Switzerland, but after what happened to the boy Mark last time I thought it prudent to turn to the less controversial topic of slimming.

Van der Pump isn't due back from his safari trip with Big Ears so I'm afraid I can't give you a definite yea or nay on our South African jaunt. Glad to see PWB is 49% ahead of the National Front. As Mrs Van der K. said on the blower the other night, thank God there's still one oasis of sanity in this mad world.

Yours in the padded cell,

DENIS

 10 Downing Street
Whitehall

17 APRIL 1987

Dear Bill,
As you may have gathered from the *Telegraph*, the Boss has been treading on air ever since she got back from Moscow with Howe and the charabanc full of reptiles. I can't make it out myself. She apparently went on their equivalent of the Terry Wogan

Show saying they were all a lot of mad warmongers, and they didn't agree about a single thing. But everyone was unanimous in saying that it was the biggest success in international diplomacy since Prosser-Cluff burned down the Naafi at Kuala Lumpur.

I asked Boris to explain it from a Russian point of view and he said it was all to do with something called 'Glasvodka' which means the new spirit abroad, i.e. a better deal for those being held in Soviet torture chambers. He said, pretty shrewdly I thought, that it must make a change for the Boss to go walkabout and be greeted by a lot of old Tory working-class babushkas waving rosaries and calling her Tsarina. A far cry from the usual hell of tomatoes and rotten eggs from Trotskyite students patting the top of her limo with sledgehammers. No wonder she went round looking like something out of *The Sound of Music*.

As for Beau Gorblimov, he's turning out to be another Mitterrand, sending round wheelbarrows full of daffs every morning from the Russian Embassy, toy Soviet spaceships and wooden dolls for Mark and Carol and – this, I think, speaks volumes for Soviet Intelligence – a daily crate of Warrington Vodka labelled 'With comradely greetings to your elderly husband'. As if that isn't enough, he's on the blower every day, with Boris roped in to translate on the extension in the Butler's Pantry, asking for tips about how to deal with the Czechs. If you ask me, which no one ever does, he won't last. They've had that sort of chap before. Think they can change the system and end up working as a lavatory attendant in some one-horse town in Outer Mongolia.

Anyway, thanks to the *Doctor Zhivago* coverage on the media, the Boss's ratings shot through the ceiling and Munster and the Corsicans went bananas, clamouring for an early kill. Indeed the Ops room was already tuned up for a lightning strike when that ghastly Dr Death apparently got wind of it and announced that M. was 'going to go on May 7th'. Result, May 7th had to be crossed out. Back to the drawing board.

If you ask me she doesn't know what the hell she's doing, just like last time. I overheard a heated exchange between M. and the plumper of the Saatchi Brothers only the other night as I was taking the cat out for a walk. 'Don't hurry me, Alberto!' a familiar voice was heard from behind blinds in the Den. 'This is an important decision, which will be made here in Downing Street and not in Fleet Street.' 'But Prime Minister,' riposted the Latin Svengali, 'if your aim, as you say, is to wipe out the

'. . . Dr Death . . . announced that M. was "going to go on May 7th" . . .'

dread menace of Socialism once and for all, then recognise this Doctor as your friend. Tebbit's attacks have built him up no end . . .' 'Leave Norman out of this,' exploded M. 'He has been overwrought and not his normal self. Socialism will be destroyed but only when I decide. The Labour Party has a long and honourable history, whatever we may think of its present-day exponents. Let us not impetuously snuff out a historic flame.'

Matters were not improved at this moment by the arrival of Luigi who burst in with a rustle of papers, announcing a fresh initiative by the Doctor. 'He admires your patriotism, Prime Minister, he would even be prepared – and here I quote – "to come to a working arrangement with the Tories in the event of a hung Parliament".' 'Ha!' was the shrill response from Margaret. 'Takes two to tango, Luigi. You can tell your Doctor my card is full. Mr Kinnock has a point when he calls him Doctor Judas. Even Hattersley was prepared to stand and fight when the pudding plates began to fly.' All in all, as you can tell, we are no further forward with deciding our holiday arrangements.

Van der Pump has come back looking fit and bronzed from

jogging through the Kalahari with Prince Bigears, but like all these tealeaf-readers he's trying to hedge his bets in case the Favourite rolls over on his back as the tapes go up. M. was out opening something on Saturday when he rang, so I had to take his message. I may have had a few, so it probably isn't quite as coherent as it might be, but what I noted on the memo pad was 'When Moon full and Bats fly North, Great Mother must cover her Feet.' This could mean practically anything. If you ask me, Van der P. may have been knocking back the embalming fluid himself. Anyway the Old Hermit has now shuffled off to meditate in the Hotel Excelsior, Gstaad (shower and shared toilet £450 a night).

Re Bank Holiday Monday. Charlie Whackett was pressing me in the Club this morning to join him for a day's stock car racing on his spread down at Virginia Water. Maurice is coming and the Major's asked us to pencil him in. You're allowed to wear a helmet and the Boys in Blue turn a blind eye to alcohol levels in the blood as part of their Community Policing Policy. Could make a change from going round at Worplesdon.

Vrum vrum,
  Yours aye,

DENIS

10 Downing Street
Whitehall

1 MAY 1987

Dear Bill,
I hope you and Maurice got back all right from the Theme Park on Bank Holiday Monday. Why those stupid buggers told me it was stock car racing I have no idea. On arrival we were strapped into the kit, had a few snorts, and were then installed behind the steering wheel. Imagine my alarm, when the starting pistol went, to find we were afloat and heading for the rapids, reptiles with flash cameras leering at us from every bend in the water-chute. I'm sorry I didn't have time to warn you, and I hope

your ducking had no nasty after-effects. There's a limit to what one should do to raise money for Charlie Whackett and his philanthropic schemes, whatever he may have done in the past to bale out the boy Mark.

Boris, who has had his ear to the keyhole more than I have, came in on Easter Sunday morning and told me that it was definitely June. Van der P. had given the green light after one of his dreams in the Alps, and they're even talking about bringing Parkie and Tarzan back on board to help organise the teas. I said why not Archer as well, and while they were about it Profumo, not to mention the one with the dark glasses who was caught in bed with a teddy bear and a couple of tarterinos? Boris had a quiet snigger at this and said there were many risks attached when black sheep are readmitted to the dacha – some old Russian saw he no doubt picked up at his grandmother's knee.

Talking of the Russkies, Hoppo seems to have run into an unexpected snarl-up with his plan to leave us to the mercies of the Bear. All along, the old boy's handlers have been urging what they call in their stupid lingo the Zero Factor, i.e. you scrap yours and we'll scrap ours – never thinking it would happen. Come Glasvodka, however, Gorblimov, who's quite a cunning little fellow with a University Degree in Accountancy, decides to call his bluff, whereupon all is confusion. Hoppo, keen to go out while he's ahead and still relatively compos, mutters about wanting to do a deal, immortality assured as the Peacemaker. Top Brass, Heavy Industry, and the miscellaneous fatcats who are doing very well as Merchants of Death servicing the warheads, get distinctly jumpy, as does the Boss, who likes to be tucked up at night thanking God for Mummy and Daddy and the dear Cruise Missiles at Greenham Common Amen. (I expect Bosendorfer, that shrink friend of the Widow Glover, would have something to say about it.)

The only change envisaged in Margaret's next Ten Year Plan is that poor old peg-leg Hailsham is finally to be booked into the Funny Farm, and they're thinking of moving Mogadon Man onto the Woolsack in his stead, thus killing two birds with one stone. Mogadon, despite his somnolent mien and brothel creepers, has always been down in the Boss's book as an ambitious little sod who would have a knife between her shoulder blades before you could say Kenneth Robinson. What better way to shunt him over the hard shoulder than to give him a peerage and a long moth-eaten old wig, and let him dodder away his declining

'. . . Boris . . . told me that it was definitely June . . .'

years listening to a lot of Bishops holding forth about condoms? Long distinguished service to the nation, summit of his profession, great historic office of state and up yours matey.

If you ask me, Moggo will be reluctant to go along with this scenario. His wife is very pushy, and has a wistful way of looking at the fixtures and furnishings at Chequers that I have never liked. It will be interesting to see how he tries to wriggle out of it.

Not a word to the Missus, but the Think Tank is working into the night on plans to flog off more of the family silver. The latest candidate is British Rail, for which Margaret has always had a particular aversion, ever since the time we were held up at Derby for three hours on the way to Cardiff. Relieved of the burden of state subsidy, this would free many mainline routes for use as motorways. It makes obvious sense, but they don't want it to get out until the nation's commuters have put their little X in the right box. Meanwhile you'll be glad to hear that the Channel Tunnel has once again run into the sand due to M's somewhat parsimonious attitude to rail travel, so you may not have to sell up your Broiler Farm at Folkestone after all.

Don't you find all these Bank Holidays very confusing? Given the profit the Banks are making, I suppose it's amazing they ever go to work at all.

Yours on deposit,

DENIS

10 Downing Street
Whitehall

15 MAY 1987

Dear Bill,
Thank you for your surprise 72nd Birthday parachutogram. The young lady was arrested in the Chequers shrubbery but the message got through loud and clear. I must say the entire Cabinet arriving in limos to be told the election date is not one's idea of an ideal birthday treat but perhaps we can celebrate when I am 77 unless I get time off for good behaviour.

As things stand all the bookies are giving short odds on the Boss. Though there is one slight cloud on the horizon. I don't know of you've been following this Tinker Tailor business about MI5 but I must say it's left me wholly mystified. Our side were clearly confident that everything had been tidied under the rug when this new newspaper run by the man with the double-barrelled name who escaped from the *Daily Telegraph* suddenly published a huge slab of Wright's memoirs claiming there had been a plot by MI5 to 'destabilise' Wilson, though from what I remember of him after a couple of large brandies he wouldn't have needed much of a push. At this Havers, who'd been through it all before when Armstrong had to toddle off Down Under, ups and slaps injunctions on all and sundry, no doubt on orders from my sleeping partner (ex).

One lesson they've never learned is that throwing a blanket over a roaring fire is the best way to burn the house down. (Also Havers seems pretty destabilised himself at the moment.) Anyway, Smellisocks, for whom things had hardly been coming up roses, saw the chance of a bit of mischief and persuaded old Callaghan, who's been on a high ever since H.M. the Q. tapped him on the shoulder with the EPNS, to do his Elder Statesman bit and demand a full-dress perusal of the dirty laundry a la Hoppogate. The Boss got very angry at this and stormed out of the Chamber, having told them that there wasn't a shred of truth in any of the stories and that she had it on the authority of the aptly-named Sir Anthony Duff, Head of Dirty Tricks, that at no time had little Wilson had his phone interfered with by the spooks.

I don't know anything about this Duff cove personally, but the last chap M. placed her confidence in turned out to be a rum 'un who took to hanging around low Belfast niteries and following bus drivers into the Gents, no doubt under pressure of work.

Funnily enough, Maurice and I were pushing the trolley round at Moor Park last week and at the bar afterwards we got talking to a chap with a moustache and an eyepatch called Fairclough-Byng, who found out who I was and, after a few large ones, took me for a walk on the lawn. He turned out to be an ex-MI5 man, adding with a weird look in his remaining eye, 'Actually old boy none of us is ever ex in this game.' He said he'd been number two to Wright during the Wilson period with a special brief for observing Russian penetration. According to him, the man who made Wilson's raincoats, Kaplan or some such name, was a General in the KGB and was in and out of Number Ten like a

*'. . . a chap with a moustache and eyepatch
called Fairclough-Byng . . .'*

yo-yo swigging down the electric soup with the then Prime
Minister as if there were no tomorrow. Fairclough-Byng had fitted
Kaplan up with a transmitter and said the conversation was often
very incoherent, but he was pretty certain from what they were
saying that they had murdered Hugh Gaitskell, so that Wilson
as Moscow's man would get the job. The Israelis somehow came
into it, via some publishing chappie, whose name didn't ring a
bell, but I can't remember how. Anyway, it all made pretty good
sense to me at the time. Fairclough-Byng said they had a patriotic
duty to keep tabs on the rotten apples and, when the time came,
to lance the boil. Unfortunately we went back to the bar after that
and during the course of the afternoon and evening it all got a
bit fuzzy at the edges.

Brooding about it on the Hendon bypass, I came to the
conclusion that these MI5 chaps had been absolutely right and
that the sooner M. knew about it the better. I found her closeted
with her new hairdresser, Monsieur Melvyn, and not in the most

receptive mood for Fairclough-Byng's important disclosures. I spilled the beans as succinctly as I could in the circs, pointing out that F-B and his merry men had only been doing their patriotic duty as they saw it, ridding the country of the Red Menace and paving the way for a new era of sound money and a return to Victorian Values under her own enlightened sway. To my surprise and that of Monsieur Melvyn, M. became very red in the face, said she was not interested in scraps of drunken tittle-tattle from inebriated riff-raff who spent the working day loafing about golf clubs and that this man, whoever he claimed to be, was certainly an impostor. She then ordered Monsieur Melvyn to lower a metal hood over her head, adjusted a visor and turned on the hairdryer at full blast, thus rendering further conversation extremely laborious. All the same, I can't help feeling something jolly rum is going on.

Mrs Van der Kafferbescher rang me last week in very high spirits to say that PWB had swept home, trouncing the pinkoes including that Ambassador chap they had over here for a bit who I always thought was unsound. They had a big party going on in the background with a lot of flamenco dancing and bottles being thrown, so I couldn't hear exactly what she was saying, but I think it was something to the effect that if M. got in for a third term why didn't she disenfranchise all the ethnics and make if a one party state. Very sound as usual, but I wonder whether people are ready for it.

Yours on the campaign trail,

DENIS

10 Downing Street
Whitehall

29 MAY 1987

Dear Bill,

Thank you for your very flattering p.c. following my TV address
to the nation on News At Ten, featuring an intimate behind-the-
scenes glimpse of our day-to-day life at Downing Street. As you
may have noticed, we had to drag in one of Lawson's spotty little
offspring to add a touch of 'caring domesticity', no grandchildren
having sprung to date from the loins of our terrible twins.

My own role, as I trust you observed, was one of studied
incompetence, hoping as I did thereby to avoid any further
exercises of that nature. 'Try to look as if you're enjoying yourself,
Denis!' the Boss hissed through gritted teeth, as they prepared
for their tenth 'take'. According to the Saatchi script, I was
supposed to be 'leafing eagerly' through my week-at-a-glance golf-
lover's diary, anxious to fix a date for a fictional holiday for two
in Cornwall. 'Won't it be fun?' shouted the Boss 'Just the two of
us! A whole week in Cornwall. You'll be able to play your golf,
won't you darling?' I was then meant to say, 'Oh yes, what fun
that will be. I can't wait!'

On the first take, I rather mucked it up by improvising the line
'Sod that for a lark. Better than the Widow Glover, I suppose,
and her awful shrink friend Bosendorfer!' At this Luigi Saatchi
seemed rather displeased, and said, 'Please Mr Thatcher, say what
is on the script if you do not mind, it will be quicker for us all
in the end.' Second go, my glasses fell off, and the third time my
throat went dry and they had to bring in a throat spray. After
that they left it all to the Boss, and just a few shots of me nodding
like a half-wit.

Quite honestly, Bill, I've taken a decision about the Third
Term. M. got completely carried away just before the whistle
blew, and said her plan was to go on and on and on, just like Herr
Hitler. You may remember he was all set to run on till the two
thousand nine hundred and thirties, but came unstuck. Since then
I've become distinctly uncooperative. I told the Boss it was all
very well for her to go on and on, but some of us were getting
a bit long in the tooth for that kind of thing, and I'd also spent

'. . . I was supposed to be "leafing eagerly" through my
week-at-a-glance golf-lover's diary . . .'

a lot of money on the insulated liquor store at Dulwich. When, I asked, rhetorically as it turned out, was I going to get a chance to enjoy the fruits?

To begin with, everything looked pretty gloomy, with our lot way ahead in all the polls, and Smellisocks in danger of being annihilated by Batman and Robin coming to the rescue in their yellow bus. In the last few days, however, sanity has begun to return, and there are, thank God, one or two hopeful indications of a Labour Landslide.

Munster's Manifesto, though containing in my view some very sound ideas like weeding out Trot schoolteachers, cleaning up the TV and privatising the water supply, has failed to find much favour with the punters, however much the Boss went on about her belief in our Great National Health Service and her caring approach to the Ethnics and the Downtrodden.

The Corsican Twins have meanwhile decreed that the Boss should play the part of the busy Prime Minister, too preoccupied with affairs of war and peace to step down into the dusty gladiatorial arena or bother with the likes of Pillock. However you may be sure, if they lose a few more points, this approach will be rapidly jettisoned and the Boss will be in there playing as dirty as the next man.

Have you seen these Smellisocks on the telly by the way? Maurice's friend Barny Hoddinot in Sevenoaks has made a killing sending up thousands of boxes of red roses every day from his glass houses, and they all wear them. This means they have to wear suits to put them in, which makes them look pretty daft, though I must say those two prize prats Dave 'n' Dave riding round in their bus really get my goat. Perhaps after all I should do my patriotic duty and reconcile myself to the idea of turning my toes up in harness. I hope you and your Lady will come and pour a libation over the tomb of the Unknown Sozzler.

I think I may be getting morbid. Boris has been very assiduous with the Plum Vodka during the last few days and it does from time to time make me sentimental. Talking of which, I gather that Smarmy Cecil has definitely been put under contract for the next four years in some kind of 'walker' capacity for the Boss. They won't let him into the Cabinet, but he can hover about outside the door with ear to the keyhole, except when little Miss Keays is parading up and down outside with her perambulator demanding justice for the unmarried mother.

Charlie Whackett has asked me along to launch the Flagship

of his new Tastee-Bit Hamburger Chain shortly after the election, and after all he's done for the boy Mark over the years I feel it's the least I can do. After that, what say you and I slip away for a couple of days R & R in the Algarve to celebrate the rebirth of Socialism?

DENIS